SPICEWORLD
THE EXHIBITION

The catalogue is published to coincide with the touring exhibition
Spiceworld: The Exhibition

Published by Kroma Press
Heritage View,
Huddersfield,
HD3 3BP

www.kromapress.com

Designed by Designers Front
Printed by Northend

ISBN: 978-0-9567685-0-6

CONTENTS

COLLECTING CULTURE
NICHOLAS ODDY

Collecting anything to the level of the contents of this exhibition is an all-consuming activity and the lower down the cultural pecking order the object of collecting is, the more difficult it becomes to convince people it is worthwhile. Yet it is the collector who is usually first out there to attempt to record and preserve the archival object, the hard evidence of human activity in the past. For this valuable service, they get little credit from all but a few other collectors of the same sort of thing. Historians despise their object fetishism, and accuse their methodology of subjectivity; current makers see more buoyant sales amongst the dead, rather than the living; even other collectors are likely to look askance through disdain, envy, taste, or a mixture of the three. Those further away from the activity perceive it in shades of darkness, harmless hobby at one end, a clear sign of psychological imbalance at the other. Jean Baudrillard in his book *The System of Objects* (1968) says that it 'is men in their forties who seem most prone to the passion', raising ageist, sex and gender issues[1]. It might be noted that the fact that Sigmund Freud was a collector does not prevent all manner of cod Freudian analyses being directed at collectors.

So; speaking as historian, one-time maker and middle-aged, male collector, a collection of Spice Girls memorabilia is a challenge. It is certainly not high art; the culture it represents is truly transient, and gendered female, either c11 years old, or now coming on 30. In design terms it is certainly powerful, but my taste tells me I do not quite like it...it gets the kitschometer needle flickering. One could (and does) ask other questions too. Has its moment passed? Is this a last gasp before the subject of the objects disappears into a zigga-zig-ah-obscurity, only to be recalled by a few pensioners in a couple of generations' time to the embarrassment of their care-home staff? On the bottom line...is it all a bad investment?

I have no doubt that all these questions and more will be being mentally posed by all but the most committed Spice Girlophiles as they wander round, and I have no doubt that avarice and envy will cause disquiet amongst many of those. But, at the same time, one is privileged to be shown a collection such as this. For a start it has the benefit of being a life-times mission, stretching across the entire potential age-span, by someone nowhere near forty and certainly not gendered male, but with all the focus, drive and commitment of Baudrillard's stereotype. As such, it seems a bit of a rarity... something that collectors tend to like. Many collectors are a bit secretive, not given to public display on the level of this. It is always impressive to see any serious collection of objects brought together, one can consider both the range of quality and design, and the methodologies of marshalling it into a cohesive whole in comfort.

The objects here represent two ends of a spectrum. At one end is the brick-in-the-wall definitive collecting methodology that underlies the mass-produced licensed and unlicensed merchandise; its range is finite and its boundaries easily defined. Empirical evidence alone will establish relative rarity, the product quality and visual impact will then determine desirability. This is the stuff of popular collecting. At the other end is the one-off material such as stage costumes. By default this cannot be 'popular' by the limitations of the nature of the objects. It resists being marshalled into an easy tick-box methodology and therefore it demands a more

rarefied conniosseurial approach, in which provenance and more abstract contextual qualities associated with it move into a much more significant place in the collector assessment. A further complexity is provided by the direct association this material has with the famous.

And here lies a serious issue, what is seen here is a collection of hard objects that represent at one step removed something largely aural and ephemeral. Recordings exist of course, but they fail to have the up-front visual impact of memorabilia. In the same way the costumes lack the performers for whom they were designed. Thus, while the musical contribution of the Spice Girls might disappear into the mists of time, the flotsam and jetsam of their popularity will continue to wash up on the shores of the collecting world, a never ending reminder of something that many critics deem forgettable. As time goes on and the original currency of the objects gets ever more distant, will they even really represent the musical phenomenon of the Spice Girls? Or will they better serve as examples of various elements of popular culture of the 1990s, be it the bizarre take on second generation feminism represented in 'girl power', to the cool Britannia of Ginger's retro-sixties, union flag garments. Whatever, collections make the task of future generations a lot easier. Whether all this material will prove to be a bad investment in monetary terms, only time will tell, but its appearance here suggests that at least it will survive to tell its tale, when most other Spice Girliana will be lost in the mire of Michael Thompson's stage of transience between 'rubbish' and 'durability' that is its position at present[2].

There will be those who look at all this and think, 'what a waste of time, if only she had invested the same effort and resource into something serious...'. To them one has to point out that the world is awash with people pouring effort and resource into what might be considered 'something serious', be it impressionist paintings, eighteenth century silver or whatever else tickles the fancy of the cultural capital of the elite. There is no need for any more, nor for more in their army of acolytes in museums, universities, auction rooms and consultancies. Instead, in this post-modern world where we are meant to perceive all culture as equal in the terms of immediate context, perhaps we need to encourage more serious collectors of things not deemed serious?

Notes:
[1] Translated in John Elsner and Roger Cardinal (eds) *The Cultures of Collecting* 1994, p9.
[2] Michael Thompson *Rubbish Theory – The Creation and Destruction of Value* (1979)

MAREK ROMANISZYN IN CONVERSATION WITH LIZ WEST

Marek Romaniszyn	Liz; you have been accumulating Spice Girls memorabilia for many years and have, arguably, one of the largest collections in the world. Can you remember when you first became interested in collecting?
Liz West	My passion for collecting began when I was about seven years old. There must have been a collector's instinct in me. My dad was a record collector, he had shelves of records and CDs, living with him probably had some effect on me.
MR	What were the first items that you remember collecting?
LW	Anything that I could gather in large quantities appealed to me. I collected nail polish, which I ordered and arranged on my windowsill according to colour gradation. I also collected beads. Anything girlie. At that age I was searching for something to collect.
MR	Then along came the Spice Girls...
LW	They certainly came along at the perfect time for me. I didn't start collecting their merchandise immediately. It wasn't until the release of their second album that I started buying all the different versions of the singles. For the first year of their existence I was purely a fan, singing their songs into my hairbrush!
MR	I do believe that everyone has an urge to collect. It just depends how much you exercise that urge, and obviously you've exercised it fully. Because of your strong desire to

collect, and the way the Spice Girls were marketed, were they the ideal subject matter to fuel your urge to collect?

LW   Certainly. In the late '90s you could walk into almost any shop and there would be shelves full of Spice Girls products. For a child collector this was a dream, and at the same time, a nightmare. I had the urge to have one of everything, but with £3 a week pocket money I had to restrain myself. However, I quickly built up a collection of inexpensive and accessible merchandise.

MR   Did you save week by week for something special or did you spend more erratically?

LW   At the time I didn't think I was spending erratically. The urge to buy was so strong that I could not wait until I had saved enough for more expensive items, so these items were put on my present wish list.

MR   What were the first Spice Girls items you remember collecting?

LW   In October '97 I bought the single 'Spice Up Your Life'. This was the first time I'd bought one of their singles. In fact there were two versions of it and I bought them both. I remember after Christmas '97, spending my gift money on anything and everything endorsed by the Spice Girls. At that point the market was saturated and so it was quite easy to spend large amounts of money.

MR	Did you begin by purchasing items most young girls were buying, for example, the odd single or perhaps a doll. And as you got one, you ended up thinking, 'I want the full set'?
LW	Yes, I bought the pencils cases just like all my school friends. Unlike them, however I kept everything in the packets, unopened and pristine. It then became a challenge to collect full sets of everything. For example, I bought an almost complete set of Spice Girl dolls in the January '98 sale in Hamleys toyshop, the Melanie C doll was missing. It then became a challenge for me to complete the set, which I finally managed seven years later.
MR	It's fascinating that at this age you would spend your money on items, which you would leave intact in their packaging. What did you then do with the merchandise?
LW	I arranged the collection on shelves; sometimes I laid the whole collection out on my bedroom floor and took photographs of it before re-organising it back on the shelves.
MR	Could you see a significant difference between your own and your friends collecting habits?
LW	Yeah, I was more competitive and obsessive. They would trade Spice Girls cards in the playground, I don't think they were too concerned if they didn't get the full set, but I was!

MR | Certainly one of the most fascinating aspects of the Spice Girls phenomenon is that they were marketed in nearly every way possible, there were even drinks with their names on. It was the idea that you could almost own a piece of the Spice Girls and consume them in every way!

LW | That idea was quite important to me as a child. I bought the Spice Girls branded Christmas crackers, handkerchiefs, cola, photo frames, etc... Naively at this point I thought I was *the* biggest Spice Girls collector and I quite liked that!

MR | There was an awful lot built on the music such as the distinctive clothes and platform shoes. There was a big element of '70s glam rock in them. They appealed to youngsters...

LW | The Spice Girls became a real life cartoon. People would say they were tacky and dressed inappropriately, but I didn't see that. I just saw larger than life characters. It helped that they had nicknames: Scary, Baby, Ginger, Sporty and Posh.

MR | Like a superhero, they each had their own character traits. Each had her own assigned persona; the girls then lived within that realm, didn't they?

LW | Yes certainly, it meant you could pick your favourite. It was a conversation piece, 'Who's your favourite Spice Girl?' Just for the record, before you ask, I don't have one. I like them equally.

MR	Did you ever incorporate the notion of collecting, or the Spice Girls into your work while you were studying at The Glasgow School of Art?
LW	You could say that the act of collecting played a part in the work I developed as an art student, though the Spice Girls did not. I wrote my dissertation on the nature of rock and pop memorabilia as 'collectables'. I wanted to learn about the psychology of collecting.
MR	At this point, were you still actively collecting?
LW	Yes, but I found it slightly embarrassing because it was unfashionable to collect the Spice Girls; everyone had moved on. People thought I was wasting my money. However, by now I was addicted and determined, collecting had become a passion.
MR	It's your drive to collect that has kept you going. My Guitar teacher once said to me, 'whichever band you first ever get into, you will never ever be able to forget them. Even if you try to not follow them, you will always keep an ear to the ground to see what they're doing and you'll still end up buying their music, because you feel loyal to them, because they are the beginning'... I certainly think how your obsession has flowered is interesting because as a young girl, like many other young girls, the Spice Girls gripped you. However, after their peak, when they tailed off, you still continued collecting...

LW | The thing was, and you could call it a mistake, I decided that when the girls started their solo careers, I would collect their solo material.

MR | Now that you are also collecting items of the five individual girls, is there more of a financial pressure because their products are probably more expensive, less disposable objects, like Victoria Beckham's branded perfume and handbags?

LW | Initially I just bought their music. However, I couldn't resist buying other products they developed. Victoria Beckham's projects began costing me a fortune. It became a challenge. I've recently decided to take a step back from collecting their solo memorabilia. Now I give priority to Spice Girls objects, with emphasis on the one-offs.

MR | I think one of the most significant elements of your collection is the clothes worn by the girls. When did you begin to buy these items?

LW | I began to acquire the costumes and outfits in 2005 as a second year undergraduate student. The first item of clothing I bought was a blue Whistles t-shirt worn by Melanie C, this featured in the artwork for her solo album 'Beautiful Intentions'. To own a personal item of clothing was particularly exciting. My collection gradually changed from being one predominantly made up of cheap shop bought merchandise to become really extensive and varied, consisting of the girls clothes, footwear, jewellery and award discs.

MR | Did acquiring one-off items and expanding your collection inspire you to approach venues to host exhibitions of your memorabilia?

LW | Partly. During my degree I became interested in the prospect of a career working in museums, therefore I undertook a placement at Paisley Museum and Art Gallery. I worked alongside the Keeper of Art and discussed my collection with her. She thought that people would be interested in seeing the costumes and outfits worn by the group. This was when I first realised the potential to exhibit my collection in museums.

MR | Having secured exhibitions and worked alongside experienced curators, have you revised the way you collect?

LW | Yes, the advice I have received from curators has been invaluable particularly in regard to methods of presentation, conservation, cataloguing and archiving. I gained an insight of how to structure a collection in a more focused and pragmatic manner. I have become more aware of the importance of selecting and buying key items that tie the whole collection together. At the back of my mind whenever I find an item, I consider; 'How will this look in a museum?', 'How important is the item?', 'Will it be remembered by someone visiting the exhibition?', and if the answer is 'No', then I don't buy it!

MR | You have gone on to catalogue your collection comprehensively, haven't you?

LW | Yes, when you have over three thousand items you can lose sight of what you have and haven't got. Although I think I'm capable of remembering the entire collection, I have often bought duplicates by mistake. It's a lot easier to check if I have an item in my collection now that I've got a database.

MR | The Spice Girls are more than nostalgia for you. There's never been a break in your collecting, you have followed them through, watched their reunion...

LW | Yep, that was a nightmare! Everyone kept saying, 'The Spice Girls are going to reunite, are you looking forward to it?' and I would say, 'No! Obviously I can't wait to see them live, but can you imagine all the new stuff I'm going to have to collect?' However, I behaved myself when I went to the reunion concert, I stood in front of the merchandise stand and picked out maybe two or three items to buy, having judged which items I thought might become rare.

MR | Being much more selective is definately a sign of maturity as a collector. Has there been any point where you have felt your urge to collect the Spice Girls has been detrimental?

LW | Definitely! As any collector will know, it can become quite an obsessive pursuit. As a collector, your value system shifts, for example; I have always preferred to buy Spice Girls items than things for myself, such as clothes. I have given absolute priority to Spice Girls items, without exception.

MR   How do you see the collection developing a public profile beyond the exhibition at Leeds City Museum?

LW   The Leeds exhibition is my third in Yorkshire and by far the largest to date. Preparing for the Leeds exhibition has been challenging and interesting. I would very much like to take the collection to other venues both in Great Britain and overseas. I will certainly continue to develop and add to the collection, though this will be done with growing consideration.

MR   What do you want the public to derive from your exhibition?

LW   I would like people to recognise the importance of the Spice Girls phenomenon within the British cultural climate of the '90s. Popular music is directly related to people's personal histories and whilst the Spice Girls connect with my own youth, I hope the exhibition will act as a trigger to allow the public to recall past memories. Also, I hope other fans will enjoy being able to take a close look at this vast collection.

MR   Lastly, you said earlier that you are going to continue collecting Spice Girls memorabilia. So, do you think you will ever collect anybody or anything else, or are you just going to stick to the Spice Girls?

LW   I think I have set myself quite a challenge with the Spice Girls and that is quite enough for me!

(Marek Romaniskyn is Assistant Curator of Community History, Leeds Museum and Galleries)

COSTUMES AND OUTFITS

Emma Bunton, *Brit Awards*, Earls Court Arena, London, 24th February 1997
Blue sequin stretch halter neck mini dress, with microphone pocket attached to the back of the dress.
Designer unknown

Geri Halliwell, *The Girlie Show*, Channel 4 Studios, London, Episode 10, 1997
Gold PVC halterneck dress with splits up both sides.
Designer unknown

Mel B, *Capital FM Awards*, London, 26th March 1997
& *Spice Girls Official Magazine cover*, Issue 4, Winter 1997
Leopard print velvet trousers with matching sleeveless crop top.
Designed by Lisa Elliott

Mel B, *Smash Hits Magazine*, 1997
Black leather knee-high biker boots with leather strap and silver buckle detail around the ankle,
tightening strap with silver buckle on the calf and chunky black rubber soles and heel.
Designed by Muzo

Mel B, *Spiceworld: The Movie* and *Impulse/Cadbury's Promotions*, London, 1997
Stretch nylon and velvet tiger print boob tube.
Designer unknown

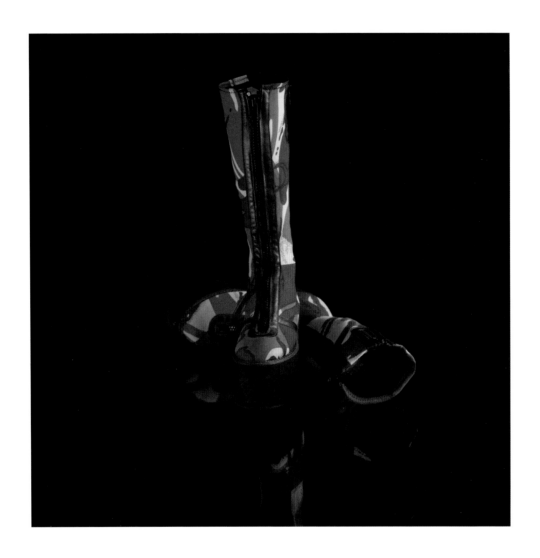

Mel B, *Spiceworld: The Movie*, 'Alien' Scene, 1997
Camouflage knee-high boots with four-inch black platform wedge sole and black zip fastening to the
front of the boot.
Designed by Buffalo
Worn with Camouflage nylon hot pant shorts with button and Velcro fastening.
Designed by Joseph (London)

Mel B , *Spiceworld: The Movie*, 'Leader of the Gang' Scene, 1997
Multicoloured striped silk two-piece suit, with exaggerated collar and long tailored jacket.
Designed by Paul Smith

Geri Halliwell, *Girl Power! Live In Istanbul Concert*, Abdi Ipekçi Arena, Istanbul, 12th and 13th October 1997
Red, white and blue Union Jack glitter finish platform ankle boots with two-inch platform sole
and four-inch heel.
Designed by Shelley's

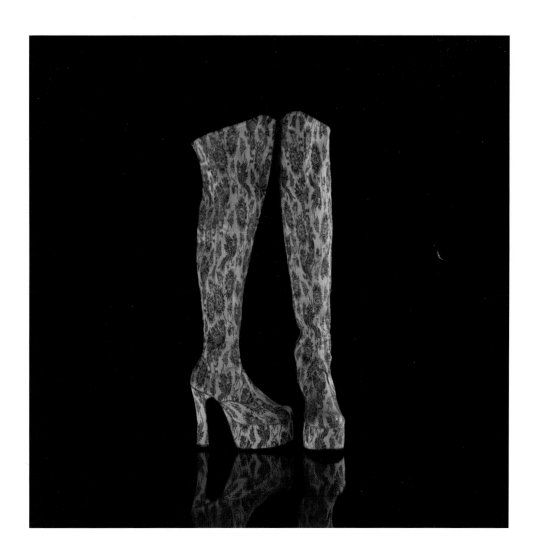

Mel B, *Girl Power! Live In Istanbul Concert*, Abdi Ipekçi Arena, Istanbul, 12th and 13th October 1997
& *MTV Europe Music Awards*, The Ahoy, Rotterdam, 6th November 1997
Lime green patterned thigh-high boots, with two-inch platform and four-inch heel.
Designed by Shelley's

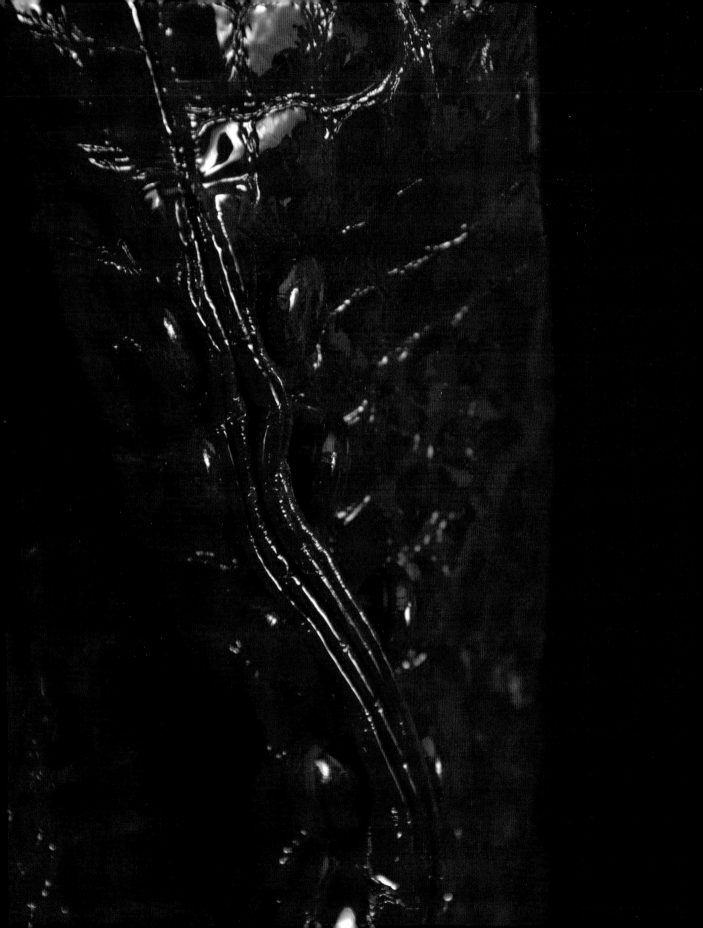

Mel B, Meeting with Nelson Mandela and Prince Charles, Official Presidential Residence, Johannesburg,
1st November 1997
Two-piece croc leather buttoned suit comprising of crimson long jacket with leather covered buttons and
bright purple satin lining. Worn with green croc leather boot cut trousers.
Designed by William Hunt

Emma Bunton, *An Audience with the Spice Girls*, Television Centre, London, 9th November 1997
Lustre finish aquamarine and green leather check pattern knee-high platform boots
with four-inch heel.
Designed by Magic Shoes (London)

Geri Halliwell, *An Audience with the Spice Girls*, Television Centre, London, 9th November 1997
Crimson velvet all-in-one catsuit with plunging halter neck and boot cut trousers.
Designed by Miss Selfridge

Geri Halliwell, *An Audience with the Spice Girls*, Television Centre, London, 9th November 1997
Black and red elasticated lace knee-length dress, with capped sleeves and V-neck line.
Satin bow to the waist.
Designed by Sue Rowe (London)

Mel B , *Royal Variety Performance*, Victoria Palace Theatre, London, 6th December 1997
Sheer tiger print gown, with cowl neckline and split up the front and back.
Designed by Maverick

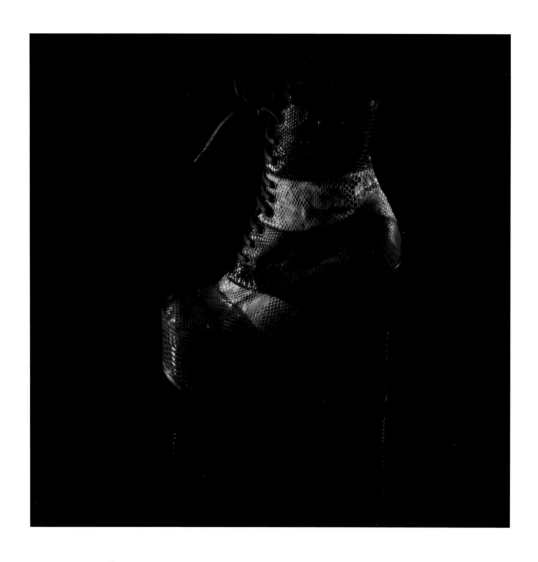

Geri Halliwell, *Billboard Music Awards*, MGM Grand Garden Arena, Las Vegas, 5th December 1997
Laced retro platform heeled ankle boots in different shades of brown, with two-inch platform sole and four-inch heel.
Designed by Buffalo

Mel B, Promotional work, 1996-97
Camouflage cotton combat style straight-leg trousers with several pockets and pouches with zip
and buckle fastenings to the front, back and sides with tightening ribbon straps to the waist.
Designed by Modo Casualwear

Geri Halliwell, Promotional work, 1996-97
Multicoloured sequin evening jacket with single button fastening.
Designed by Jean Paul Gaultier

Geri Halliwell, Promotional work, 1997
Green leather button-up trouser suit with high waist bottoms and bomber jacket style top.
Designed by Antic

Geri Halliwell, *Brit Awards*, Earls Court Arena, London, 9th February 1998
Crimson wet-look velvet mini dress with inbuilt microphone pouch to the back.
Designed by Maverick and made by Academy Costumes (London)
Worn with crimson crushed velvet knee-high boots with two-inch platform sole and four-inch heel.
Designed by Yinge Yang (Italy)

Mel B, *Brit Awards*, Earls Court Arena, London, 9th February 1998
Bright orange stretch velvet leopard print skinny fit trousers with bell bottom flare
and matching halter neck bikini bra.
Designer unknown
Worn with orange and burgundy four-inch platform soled trainers with black tread.
Designed by Buffalo

Mel B, *Stop* Video, Carnew Street, Dublin and Rathdrum, Co. Wicklow, Ireland, March 1998
Floor-length brown and orange patterned Afghan carpet coat with white tussled fluffy sheepskin lining.
Designer unknown
Worn with shiny brown wrap leather knee-high boots with sturdy two-inch platform sole
and three-inch heel.
Designed by Buffalo

Mel B, *Spiceworld Tour 1998*, (United Kingdom, Europe and Scandinavia), Act Five, 'Fosse'
Skin tone stretch body suit with polished amber crystals, orange crushed velvet hot pants with crystals
and orange glitter encrusted knee-high platform heeled boots.
Designed by Academy Costumes (London)

Geri Halliwell, *Spiceworld Tour 1998*, (United Kingdom, Europe and Scandinavia) Act Five, 'Fosse'
Glitter encrusted green stretch lycra leotard dress with satin thread tassel's, emerald crystals
and microphone pouch sewn onto the back.
Designed by Academy Costumes (London)

Emma Bunton, *Spiceworld Tour 1998*, (United States and Canada), Act One, 'Space Opening'
Pink and blue sequin nylon halterneck mini dress with polished metal 'S' on the neckline, sapphire
crystals and microphone pocket sewn onto the back.
Designed by Academy Costumes (London)

Mel B, *Spiceworld Tour 1998*, (United Kingdom, Europe and North America)
Red croc leather ankle boots with two-inch platform and four-inch heel.
Designed by Shelley's

Mel B, *Spiceworld Tour 1998*, (United Kingdom, Europe and North America) Act One, 'Space Opening'
Cream, brown and leopard print faux fur trainers, with two-inch wedged platform sole.
Designed by Buffalo

Geri Halliwell, *Spiceworld Tour 1998*, (United Kingdom, Europe and Scandinavia)
Dark blue denim ankle boots with two-inch platform and four-inch heel.
Designed by Shelley's

Spice Girls, *Spiceworld Tour 1998*, (United States and Canada)
Matching silver jump suits made for Mel B, Emma, Melanie C and Victoria.
Designed by Academy Costumes (London)

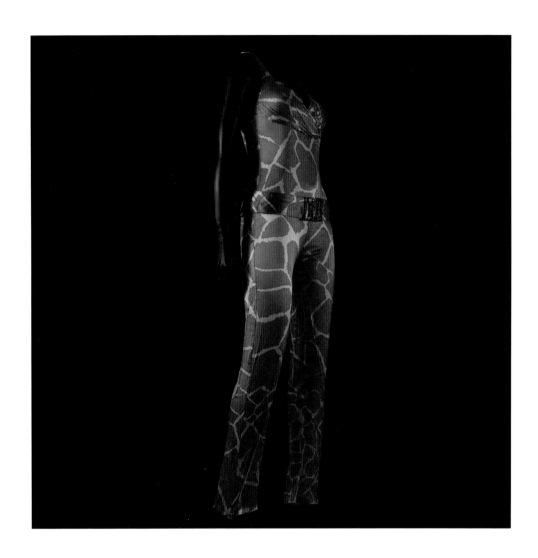

Mel B, *Return of the Spice Girls Tour 2007/08*, (United Kingdom, Europe and North America),
Act One, 'Power of 5'
Silk Giraffe print catsuit with inbuilt bra and white elastic stirrups. Worn with matching giraffe print
belt, rhinestone studded belt buckle - spelling out 'Mel B'.
Designed by Roberto Cavalli

Mel B, *Return of the Spice Girls Tour 2007/08*, (United Kingdom, Europe and North America),
Act Three, 'Bittersweet'
Black suede studded ankle boots with three-inch heel.
Designed by Jeffery Campbell

Victoria Beckham
Gold and enamel watch with pearl clock face and diamond detail.
Designed by Chopard

Geri Halliwell, *Look At Me* Video, Various Locations, Prague, March 1999
Light pink soft leather dance shoes with strap and buckle fastening, leather sole and two-inch tap heel.
Designed by Free Lance (Paris)

Geri Halliwell
Spray-painted white knee-high boots, with three-inch heel, PVC extension to make the boot taller and red leather trim to reference St. George's Cross. Customised from a pair of black leather boots.
Made by Prada

Geri Halliwell, *MTV Europe Music Awards*, The Point, Dublin, 11th November 1999
Handmade sheer sleeveless black lace beaded floor-length dress with splits up both sides
and plunge neckline.
Designed by William Baker

Melanie C, *On The Horizon* Video, Spain, June 2003
Basic plimsoll white canvas trainers with black tip on the toe.
Designed by Converse

Melanie C, *Beautiful Intentions* Album Artwork, Recording Studio, London, 2004
Light blue and grey tie-dye effect V-neck long T-shirt top with hand stitched bead, sequin and jewel
encrusted adornment on left breast and ruched sleeve straps with beaded tightening cords.
Designed by Whistles (London)

MEMORABILIA

Newspapers and Magazines
This is a selection of magazines and newspapers the Spice Girls appeared on the cover of in order to promote their singles and albums. The diverse range of publications shows how wide spread the Spice Girls success was at that time.

 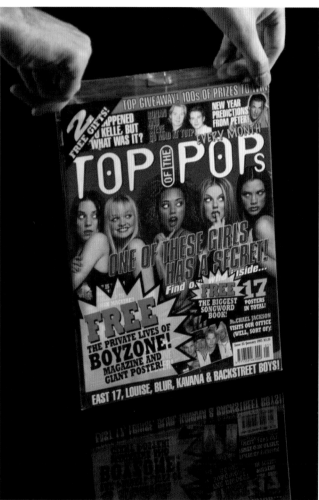

New Musical Express, 23rd November 1996
Top of the Pops Magazine, January 1997

The Sun Newspaper, 20th November 1997
The Mirror Newspaper, 22nd December 1997

Endorsement Products

The Spice Girls were famous for their merchandising, aimed at young fans. Asda supermarket, Pepsi cola, Walkers crisps, Aprilia Sonic Scooters, Impulse body spray, Polaroid cameras and Sony Playstation were just a few of the deals that the Spice Girls signed.

Set of 6 Pepsi Cans
Aprilia Scooter Helmet
Buffalo Trainers (First Prize Impulse Competition)

Impulse Shower Gel and Body Spray
Chupa Chups Giant Lolly Tin
Sealed Box of Crazy Dips and 5 Individual Packets
Walkers Cheese and Chive Multipack Crisp Bag

Polaroid Spice Cam 600 Instant Film Camera

Cadbury's Easter Eggs
Box of Cadbury's Chocolates
Set of 5 Cadbury's Chocolate Bars
Asda Merchandise; Christmas Crackers, Biscuits, Handkerchiefs and Playing Cards

Official Merchandise
The Spice Girls maximised their success by launching an official merchandise range.
This included handkerchiefs, stationary, lamps, bedspreads, dolls, bikes and dress-up sets. The Spice Girls
put their name to almost everything.

Spice Girls Official Pink Tote Bag
Spice Girls Official Lamp Shade and Base
Spice Girls Official Asda Green Silk Tie
Spice Girls Official Bike Basket

Spice Girls Official Pink Money Tin
Spice Girls Official Silver Mini Backpack
Spice Girls Official White Lunchbox and Drinks Flask

Set of 5 Individual Mugs: Scary, Baby, Sporty, Ginger and Posh

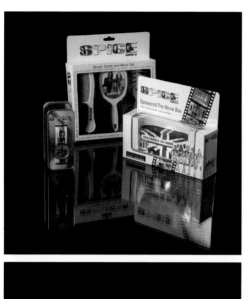

Brush, Comb and Mirror Set, Spiceworld: The Movie Bus and Zeon Watch.
Forever Spice Book
Girl Power! Book
Set of Mini Pocket Official Books

Spiceworld Playstation Game
Spiceworld Tour Teddy Bear with T-Shirt
Spiceworld Tour Pink Scarf

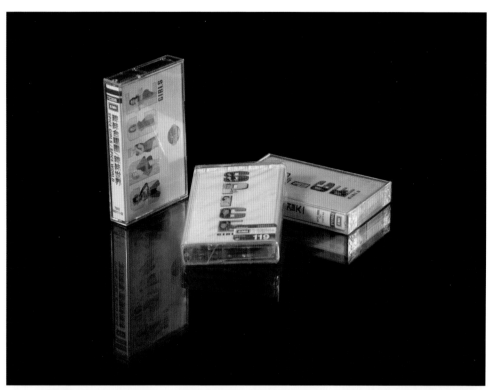

Three Cassettes (Taiwanese *Spiceworld*, Thai *Spice*, Taiwanese *Spice*)
Spice Girls Promotional Dice
Spiceworld Tour Orange and Purple Working Crew Passes
Return of the Spice Girls Tour Press Pass

Spice Girls Dolls

The original set of Spice Girls dolls was one of the most popular toys for Christmas 1997 and included miniature costumes made famous by the Spice Girls. After the success of these dolls, the manufacturers went on to release several more editions, updating the outfits and look of the dolls as time went on. When Geri left the group her doll was discontinued.

Geri Halliwell *Concert Collection* Doll
Emma Bunton *Spice It Up* Doll

Set of four *Viva Forever* Dolls with Finger Puppets.

Spiceworld: The Movie

The Spice Girls followed in the footsteps of other great rock and pop stars like Elvis Presley and The Beatles by appearing in their own movie. *Spiceworld: The Movie* premiered at the Cannes Film Festival in May 1997. To promote the film the Spice Girls attended a photo call on top of a building. They mananged to bring the traffic to a standstill just as The Beatles had done 30 years before!

Set in London and featuring a double decker bus painted with the Union Flag, the film was a box office smash hit after being released on Boxing Day in 1997. The film featured many famous faces, including Elton John, Meat Loaf, Roger Moore, Richard E. Grant, Barry Humphries, Michael Barrymore, Jools Holland, Stephen Fry, Bob Geldof, Jennifer Saunders, Hugh Laurie and Elvis Costello to name a few!

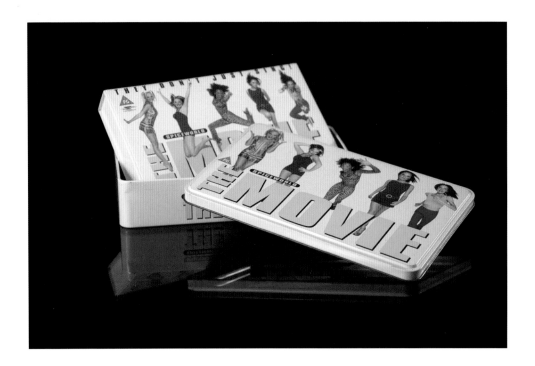

Spiceworld: The Movie UK, Group Tin and VHS

La Pelicula Spanish VHS

Award Discs

Here is a selection of award discs from around the world which were presented to important industry figures to commemorate sales of the Spice Girls albums and singles, as well as their solo achievements.

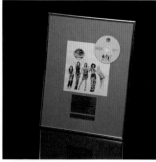

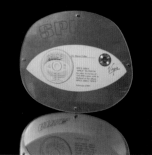

Spice Girls *Spice* Album Award
(Awarded for sales of more than three million copies
in the United Kingdom. 1997)

Spice Girls *Spiceworld* Album Award
(Awarded for sales of fifty thousand copies in Austria.
Presented to Geri Halliwell whilst on tour in Europe. 1998)

Spice Girls *Forever* Album Award
(Canadian Recording Industry Association Award
for double-platinum sales in Canada. 2001)

Spice Girls *Spice* Album Award
(Awarded to manager Simon Fuller for sales
of one hundred thousand copies in Holland. 1997)

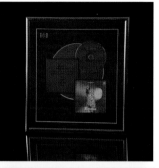

Geri Halliwell *Schizophonic* Album Award
(EMI Award for Gold Sales in Australia. 1999)

Emma Bunton *Free Me* Album Award
(Awarded for sales of more than one hundred thousand copies
in the United Kingdom. 2004)

Melanie C *Northern Star* Album Award
(Awarded for sales of more than three hundred thousand copies
in the United Kingdom. Presented to Heart FM. 1999)

Victoria Beckham *Out of Your Mind* Single Award
(Awarded for sales of more than four hundred thousand copies
in the United Kingdom. 2000)

Solo Items

Each of the Spice Girls forged individual careers, creating fashion empires, releasing music, appearing on Broadway and in the West End, hosting TV and radio shows and writing children's books.

Victoria Beckham Official White Cap, Autographed
Victoria Beckham and Samantha Thavasa Purple Leather Handbag
Victoria Beckham DVB Black Sunglasses

Victoria Beckham *Full Length and Fabulous World Cup Party*; Satin Gift Bag and Limited Edition
Engraved Motorola Phone
Geri Halliwell set of *Ugenia Lavender* Children's Books
Geri Halliwell *Scream If You Wanna Go Faster* Pink Cadillac Model Car
Geri Halliwell *Ride It* Cufflinks
Melanie C *Live At The Hard Rock Café* DVD

Credits

Collecting Culture written by Nicholas Oddy
Marek Romaniszyn in conversation with Liz West transcribed by Liz West
Description Text by Liz West

Designed by Matt West
Photography by Ben Barker
www.designersfront.com

Published By Kroma Press
www.kromapress.com